Fast
Creatures

Fast creatures

Running across the savannah in huge strides,
cutting through the air, nosediving from a great height,
or speeding through the waves like a rocket,
the animal world is full of athletes capable of remarkable speed,
whether over long or short distances.

But this athletic prowess has nothing to do
with sport or with play. It is, purely and simply,
to ensure their survival — both personal and that of their species —
that leopards, falcons and sharks are endowed
with such power, speed and stamina.

The pursuit of prey, the need to escape enemies,
the search for food or for a watering hole,
are essential requirements that determine an animal's behaviour,
and translate in certain creatures into an aptitude
for running, swimming, flying or even,
as in the case of the snail, crawling on its stomach.

The gazelle can reach speeds of up to 70 kilometres per hour.

The gazelle usually gives birth to one fawn per brood. It then leaves its young for up to three weeks, hidden in the grass, until it is old enough to follow the herd. During that time, the mother feeds it several times a day.

Small and fragile,
gazelles
run like the wind

A GRACEFUL RUNNER

The gazelle is a svelte fragile animal and is one of the most graceful known to man. Beneath this soft fragile exterior, however, lie amazing powers of stamina that enable it to survive in some of the driest regions of the world. Like the antelope of Africa and Asia, the gazelle is a ruminant and belongs to the family of Bovidae. It is the prey of animals such as cheetahs, jackals and hyenas. When faced with danger, the gazelle's best chances of survival lie in fleeing, being able to reach high speeds and outdistance its attackers. Its long powerful legs also enable it to jump vertically to a height of almost 2 metres and surprise its enemies.

All gazelles have a white patch on their rump with two vertical black lines on either side and another dividing it down the middle. This black and white pattern on the mother encourages the young fawn to follow her as soon as it is able. The mother's udders are another incentive, associated with the pleasures of feeding and safety.

Whilst it is true that gazelles can reach high speeds, they still fall prey to cheetahs, even if the latter have to accelerate to 100 or 110 kilometres per hour to do so. They usually manage to bring the gazelle down in mid-flight with a swipe of the paw.

The gazelle has a number of natural assets when it comes to protecting itself from its predators: good hearing, sharp vision and incredible speed. In what is known as a 'stotting jump', the animal jumps on the spot with its legs straight in a sort of dance that is aimed at confusing its enemy whilst warning the rest of the herd of the approaching danger.

The powerful talons of the golden eagle are a lethal weapon.

Like most diurnal birds of prey, the golden eagle has a prominent arch above its eyes, giving it a threatening air. This feature improves its vision by cutting out the dazzle from the sun and protects its eyes from the air when the bird is flying at great speed.

Like fighter pilots, **golden eagles** dive-bomb their prey

NOSEDIVING AT 300 KM/H

The golden eagle is one of 290 species of diurnal bird of prey. This born hunter capitalizes on its natural assets: outstanding vision, a sharp beak and claws of steel. Whilst gliding majestically, its large wings outspread, it is able to survey its territory with a piercing eye. On spotting its prey, it beats its wings to move lower and alter its trajectory, then folds them away in order to dive-bomb, surprising its victim in a hedge-hopping manoeuvre. In spite of the amazing speeds it can reach during one of these dives (up to 300 kilometres per hour), the golden eagle often misses its target and returns empty-handed.

Before hunting, the golden eagle waits until the ground has been sufficiently warmed by the sun's rays. This increase in ground temperature causes warm air currents to rise, enabling the bird to soar high in the sky with its wings spread wide. In this way it is able to conserve energy whilst exploring its territory.

Outside the mating season, which lasts from the end of winter to spring, the golden eagle conserves energy. It is capable of remaining motionless on its perch for more than ten hours a day. The underside of its claws are covered with scaly pads, ensuring a firm grip. As it expends less energy, the bird is able to go without food for up to a week.

A fast and powerful bird of prey, the golden eagle needs wild open spaces in order to survive. Nowadays, such areas are rarely found outside mountain ranges. The size of one birds territory will depend on the concentration of prey in the area and on the number of possible nesting sites.

With their ears forever cocked,
hares
bolt at the slightest sound

If a predator comes within 3 metres, the hare will bolt, running in a straight line and turning sharply.

A RUNNER WITH BIG FEET

The European hare is a small animal with a long slender body and inordinately large legs and ears. Its hind legs, designed for jumping, are longer and more powerful than the front pair. When it advances or jumps slowly, the hare uses the full length of its long hind legs. When it moves quickly, however, it only uses the cushions on the bottom of its feet. It is able to run in a straight line at speeds of up to 70 kilometres per hour and is also capable of turning at an angle of 90° in order to shake off its attackers.

A born runner

The European hare is one of the fastest animals around, making it possible for it to survive in areas where there are few places to hide. It can maintain a top speed of 70 kilometres per hour for up to 15 minutes. When it is forced to flee, its heart rate accelerates, ensuring that its muscles continue to perform well at high speeds.

For the first few months, leverets look like small balls of fluff with a round snout and short ears. Hares leave their leverets for two or three days after birth, then return once a day for feeding.

The snow hare of North America and Europe is brown in summer and turns white in winter. Only the tips of its ears remain black. Their winter coat helps them to hide in the snow.

In winter, the hare eats snow to quench its thirst.

A born jumper

The hare advances in leaps and bounds, pushing off on its hind legs and landing on its front ones. Its rear limbs are particularly long and powerful, enabling it to produce leaps of up to two metres, horizontally as well as vertically. According to reports, it is also able to jump to a height of 1.5 metres from a standing start.

LET'S MAKE A RUN FOR IT!

It is practically impossible to surprise a hare. With its sharp sense of hearing, the slightest noise puts it on the alert. Constantly interrupting its meal to survey the surroundings, it is ready to run for it at any time. Flight is undoubtedly the hare's best form of defence. In addition to its incredible speed and ability to change direction suddenly, it also knows how to retrace its steps, throwing its attackers off the scent. It is also an excellent swimmer and will readily jump into water to escape.

The ability to hear and see anything suspicious quickly is indispensable for a small animal like the hare that lives in wide open spaces at the mercy of its enemies. Hearing is the sharpest of this animal's senses, whilst its sight is not that strong in spite of the fact that its eyes, placed on the side of its head, give it a wide field of vision.

With a spring-loaded tongue,
chameleons
pose a threat without even moving

A PATIENT AND WELL-ARMED HIGHWAYMAN

The chameleon belongs to the order of iguanas, which includes true iguanas and agamids. It differs from the latter by the way in which it uses its tongue to hunt. The chameleon spends the day lying in wait for its prey. Its eyes are able to move independently and in different directions, enabling it to watch the ground with one whilst looking at the sky with the other. Its sticky tongue with a club-shaped end springs out like a missile to knock out any unsuspecting passer-by that has wandered too close. The animal can extend its tongue to a distance that is equal to that of its body. Furthermore, it completes this with amazing speed, capable of catching four flies in mid-flight within the space of three seconds. It takes just a fraction of a second for its tongue to unfurl, and half a second for it to curl up again. Generally speaking, the chameleon seldom misses its prey, but if it does, it will strike again as many times as necessary.

Profile

Chameleon
Chamaeleo chamaeleon
Family: Chamaeleontidae
Size: 20 cm – 48 cm

Habitat: dunes, coastal wooded areas, arid regions, shrubby savannah
Diet: insects, especially orthopterans (eg grasshoppers), dipterans (eg flies) and lepidopterans (eg butterflies)
Incubation period: 6 – 9 months
Life expectancy: several years
Predators: diurnal birds of prey (eg harriers), tree snakes

The chameleon's tongue can stretch to almost 50 cm in length. When not extended, this long sticky tube with its bulbous end is folded away like a spring around a pointed bone. The animal is capable of extending it at great speed, like a trigger releasing a coil.

Once the chameleon is sufficiently close to its prey, it opens its mouth and, with amazing speed and accuracy, unleashes its tongue, knocking out the creature with the club-shaped end. The victim of this lightning attack then finds itself stuck to the weapon, enabling the chameleon to put it in its mouth by retracting the tongue.

In order to strengthen its grip on a branch, the chameleon uses its tail as an extra form of support, creating a veritable safety catch by wrapping it round the support. The complete 'locking system' is so effective that the chameleon rarely falls from its perch.

The chameleon's tongue is a finely-tuned piece of equipment.

IDENTIFYING MALE FROM FEMALE

Male chameleons can be distinguished from females by their larger size, brighter colours and horns, known as rostrums, at the end of their snout. When these are present in the female, they are always smaller and the shape of her casque is less pronounced. A male can also be identified by the double swelling at the base of its tail, indicating the presence of the internal dual sex organ, the hemi-penis.

The tongue of an average-sized chameleon is only a dozen centimetres in length when relaxed. When extended, however, it can double in size. The nonchalant air of the chameleon is deceiving since the animal is capable of reacting with incredible speed. Its long tongue enables it to catch prey without using its claws.

Fast and powerful swimmers, **killer whales** are also capable of impressive jumps

Killer whales often adopt a lookout position. Coming to the surface, they briefly lift their head out of the water, or even raise themselves up as far as their pectoral fins, as if to survey the area around them. This activity, known as spy hopping, is sometimes performed by several animals at once.

SURPRISING AGILITY

With an estimated speed in the water of 30 knots, or 55 kilometres per hour, the killer whale is one of the fastest marine mammals along with certain larger dolphins. When it is not advancing, the killer whale is capable of lifting its enormous body out of the water, completing leaps, jumps and spectacular movements with its tail. The entire physique of the killer whale spells strength and power. Its cone-shaped head, distinctive snout and particularly its fins are all instantly recognizable. Its dorsal fin, in the shape of an isosceles triangle, can grow to a height of 1.8 m in males. In younger animals and females it is much smaller and sickle-shaped.

When the killer whale comes out of the water to breathe, it breaks the surface with the top of its head. It then breathes out noisily, sending a jet of water from its blowhole. As it breathes in, its back and triangular dorsal fin appear above the surface. Finally, the animal lowers its head and dives once again, waving its tail in the air.

In the northern hemisphere, killer whales are found along the entire Pacific coast of America and off the coast of Asia as far as Japan. In the southern hemisphere, they live mainly along the coasts of Antarctica and the southern part of South America.

The animal often lets itself fall heavily at the end of a jump, sending the water flying all around it. The way in which the killer whale beats the surface of the water with its tail is so powerful that it can be heard several kilometres away. This beating of the water is particularly common before mating.

Humming birds
can even fly backwards

The long thin beak of the humming bird is anything from 6 to 110 millimetres long, depending on the species. Its curved shape makes it easier to collect the nectar it lives on from the long corollas of flowers. It also pollinates certain flowers.

Profile

Humming bird
Cynanthus latirostris
Family: Trochilidae
Size: 10 cm
Weight: 3 g – 4 g

Habitat: dry hilly areas, wooded hillsides
Distribution: Mexico and the USA (Arizona, New Mexico)
Diet: nectar, insects
Incubation period: around 20 days
Number of young per brood: 2
Life expectancy: up to 7 years in captivity
Predators: falcons, tree snakes
There are 320 species of humming bird spread throughout America

INCREDIBLE SPEED

The humming bird is a small bird, just 6 to 11 centimetres in size. This does not prevent it, however, from being a champion flyer, capable of reaching amazing speeds: from 40 to 70 kilometres per hour for some tropical species, and up to 95 kilometres per hour with a following wind! Furthermore, it can fly forwards, hover, and even fly backwards, simply by changing the angle of its wings. Whichever method it is using, the speed with which it beats its wings is extraordinary: from 50 to 60 beats per second!

Like all birds that are born in a nest, young humming birds are not particularly well developed when they first hatch and must remain in the safety of the nest until they have finished growing.

Nectar addicts

Humming birds can be divided into five categories according to how they feed and occupy their space. 'Territorials' feed from flowers that are rich in nectar and remain within a small territory which they are prepared to defend at any cost from intruders. These birds cover little ground compared with 'trappers'. The latter are forced to travel further when feeding since they are attracted to flowers that produce less nectar. 'Non-specialists', are not satisfied with a diet of nectar alone. They also drink the juice of damaged or over-ripe fruit, and sometimes catch insects or eat those that are stuck in the juice. As well as feeding on nectar 'thieves' have

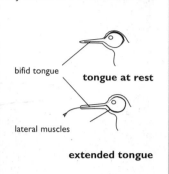

Pollen carriers

Humming birds are the only birds in America to live almost solely off nectar and because of this they play an important part in pollination. It has been shown that some flowers, particularly those that have a tubular corolla, rely on determined humming birds to pollinate large numbers of the species.

bifid tongue

tongue at rest

lateral muscles

extended tongue

been known to raid spider's webs, and steal the victims that have been caught in them. Finally, 'drillers' are forced to drill through the base of long corollas to extract the nectar since their beaks are too short to reach the bottom.

As well as being the only bird that can fly backwards, the humming bird can also hover in order to extract the nectar from the heart of the flower. Due to its powerful pectoral muscles, it is able to beat its wings so fast that the human eye cannot make out the individual movements. The humming bird relies on its wings for everything it does. It is rare to see this bird walking. It prefers to fly!

Like small horses with striped coats,
zebras
gallop away from danger

Unlike other species, male and female Grevy's zebras do not form lasting relationships. Stallions do not establish families. They prefer to take control of a particular territory, forbidding entry to any other male zebras and are prepared to fight to maintain this control. During the course of this fighting, bites to the throat, neck and legs can become vicious.

THREE AFRICAN FAMILIES

Like the ass and the horse, the zebra is part of the family of Equidae. It is found in southern and eastern parts of Africa where three different species have been identified, all of them similar in size, shape and behaviour. The plains zebra is the most common and lives mainly in Tanzania and Kenya in areas where there are a lot of national parks and game reserves. The mountain zebra, a species whose numbers are falling, is found in South Africa and Namibia. The mountain zebra is distinguishable from the plains zebra by a small pocket of skin on its neck, the function of which is unknown. It is able to cross the rocky ground of its

There are five sub-species of plains zebra, classified according to their distribution from north to south. They differ from one another by their stripes which become less distinct the further south the subspecies is found. The stripes on the rump of the mountain zebra are perpendicular to those on its body. The stripes of the Grevy's zebra are narrower and closer together.

habitat with ease thanks to its particularly hard hooves. Grevy's zebra, a species that is now almost extinct, having been hunted extensively for its beautiful coat, is mainly native to northern parts of Kenya. The Grevy's zebra is the largest and most elegant of all, measuring 1.5 to 1.6 metres to the withers.

RACES IN THE SAVANNAH

The plains zebra is well adapted to wide open spaces. Its long legs and hooves enable it to cover hundreds of kilometres in search of food. To escape its predators, notably lions and hyenas, it is capable of galloping at speeds of up to 60 km/h over short distances. That is equal to running the 100 metres in six seconds!

When the stallion senses danger, it warns the others by giving a snore-like cry. The herd comes together and flees as a group, the stallion bringing up the rear, spurring them on and even biting those that are lagging behind to make them run faster.

This plains zebra, photographed in Kenya, seems to be taking a lunchtime nap, as do most of its species between meals. Capable of dozing standing up with its head lowered, the animal will also lie down to sleep properly. Here, a cattle egret takes advantage of the situation to look for parasites in the zebra's fur.

Zebras are herbivores that cross the savannah, moving from one clump of grass to the next, covering several kilometres a day. Their meals, eaten together as a group, are spread equally over 15 hours throughout the day and night.

The vast grassy plains of the savannah cover more than a third of the surface of the African continent. These huge areas of grassland, scattered with acacias and baobabs, provide food for over 40 species of herbivore, including the zebra.

Zebras must drink at least once a day during the dry season. If a river is dry or the water too muddy, they will dig holes in the ground with their hooves to a depth of 50 centimetres, enabling them to drink clear water.

The search for water, necessary for survival, determines the annual migration of zebras, forcing them sometimes to cross hundreds of kilometres. Groups come together for these migrations, forming herds of several thousand members.

In just a few seconds,
sidewinders
paralyse their prey

A LIGHTNING ATTACK

The sidewinder is a small rattlesnake that lives in the deserts of southern America and the north-west of Mexico. Its favourite prey are mice, rats, squirrels and prairie dogs. When hunting the sidewinder lies in wait for passing prey. As soon as it sees its victim, it moves into an attacking position with its body coiled round, and its head and neck raised off the ground. The attack is carried out silently and with lightning speed. With a quick bite of its teeth, or rather two venomous fangs, it immobilizes its prey. The poison begins digesting the animal immediately, with death coming several seconds after the bite. The poisoned animal collapses paralysed after several short convulsions.

Flat and triangular, the head of the sidewinder is crowned with two horn-shaped scales which stick up above its eyes. Its eyelids are transparent and fixed over its eyes meaning that the snake always has its eyes open, even when sleeping. Above its eyes, the sidewinder has additional sense organs which enable it to see in the dark.

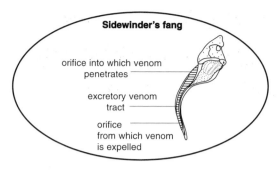

Sidewinder's fang

orifice into which venom penetrates

excretory venom tract

orifice from which venom is expelled

A FEARSOME PREDATOR

An attack by the sidewinder often gives the impression that its fangs have not properly penetrated the victim's skin. The latter may sometimes escape unharmed, if, for example, only one of the fangs has penetrated or if the dose of venom injected was insufficient. This is rare as the snake controls the amount of venom injected at one time very carefully. It is likely that the larger the prey, the more venom is used. In general, the sidewinder keeps a certain amount of venom in reserve, and only if it feels extremely frightened will it use up all its reserves in one bite. The snake's venom contains substances that digest its prey from

The sidewinder has two fangs attached to its jaw that are connected to a venom gland. At the level of the palate, small teeth help the snake to keep a firm hold of its prey. To close its mouth, the moveable jaw pivots inwards and its fangs move back against the palate.

the inside. Whilst the sidewinder always lets go of mammals, it holds on to birds, lizards and frogs with its fangs and teeth. This is because birds would be able to fly off, whilst lizards and frogs, being cold-blooded animals, are less susceptible to the venom. Occasionally, the victim is able to continue on its way once it has been bitten, but in general, it does not get very far.

As it sticks out its tongue to take in the smells around it, the small sidewinder is instantly recognizable. It is able to move its tongue rapidly backwards and forwards, even with its mouth closed. The sidewinder's tongue is around 15 millimetres long and has a forked end. The two ends of this forked tip enable it to smell things around it.

As supple as gymnasts,
California sea lions
take to the water like fish

THE 'PORPOISE' STROKE

The California sea lion is found in certain coastal areas of the north Pacific and the Galapagos Islands. It is happiest in water, even during the mating season when it is forced to spend most of its time on land.

When swimming, it propels itself forward using its front flippers with the back ones acting as a rudder. To move more quickly, the sea lion uses the 'porpoise' stroke: from time to time it comes to the surface, then arches its back and dives below again. Groups of 5 to 20 young sea lions have been seen swimming in this fashion, one behind the other, which may explain a number of alleged sightings of 'sea monsters'. The sea lion can travel at a speed of up to 30 km/h in the water and it is incredibly supple: it can change direction almost immediately and due to the flexibility of its long neck, can catch its prey without difficulty.

Sea lions are able to sleep standing up
with their head held high
and their snout pointing upwards.

There are around 150,000 California sea lions along the coasts of California and Mexico. They are not just limited to these areas, there are around 40,000 on the Galapagos Islands, south of the Equator.

Sea lions are gregarious animals. They love to snuggle up to each other, forming huge tightly-packed groups on land, even though all around them lie vast areas of empty coastline. The sight or sound of humans or anything out of the ordinary can send the entire group rushing for the sea.

Once in the water, sea lions spend their time swimming, playing and pirouetting, moving with ease thanks to the suppleness of their bodies.

The female sea lion stays in close physical contact with her young for the first few days after it is born. Immediately after the birth, the mother and young exchange cries for around fifteen minutes. These cries are repeated several times over the following hours and serve to aid mutual recognition later.

At home in the surf

Wonderfully adapted for a life spent in the water, the sea lion spends most of its time in the sea. When it comes on land, it does not choose any particular site, and it will seek refuge in the water at the slightest sign of danger. The sea lion only rarely comes on to the land outside the mating season – from May to September in the northern hemisphere. Even during this period, it makes frequent trips into the sea to refresh itself, moisten its skin, or find food: octopuses, squid, anchovies, herrings, or

The California sea lion knows how to make itself heard. The adult male has a lump on its forehead, some larger than others, that is not present in the female.

salmon. When it goes off in search of food, the sea lion makes short, shallow dives. The descents take an average of three minutes, and are to a depth of 70 metres. But the larger the sea lion, the longer the dives can be, because larger animals can hold more oxygen: large sea lions can stay under water at a depth of 270 metres for up to 12 minutes.

And riding the waves

The sea lion is skilled at using the swell of the sea to enter the water and, more importantly, to return to land. Sea lions will 'surf' a wave, letting it carry them right to the shore. It is a very playful animal and it is also quite common to see them chasing each other wildly riding the waves.

The sea lion's front limbs are significantly larger than its back ones, acting as flippers, whilst its webbed feet are used as a rudder.

Profile

The sea lion
Zalophus californianus
Family: Otaridae
Size: males from 2 m to 2.5 m; females from 1.5 m to 2 m
Weight: males from 200 to 300 kg; females from 50 to 100 kg
Habitat: coastal regions of the north and south Pacific (California, Mexico), Galapagos Islands
Diet: cephalopods (octopuses) and fish
Gestation period: 11 months
Number of young per brood: usually 1
Life expectancy: around 15 years

Elegant and fragile,
dragonflies
are the world's fastest flying insects

The flexible head of the dragonfly consists of two large eyes and three smaller eyes, known as ocelli.

ELEGANT WINGS

Along with the mayfly, the dragonfly is the last remaining member of the Palaeoptera family, the oldest group of insects known to man. Dragonflies are divided into two subspecies: *Zygoptera* and *Anisoptera*. *Zygoptera* have two sets of wings that are almost identical and are folded away when the insect is resting. *Anisoptera*, on the other hand, have sets of wings that are different from each other and are spread even when the insect is resting. All dragonflies, however, are hunters able to catch their prey in mid flight due to their speed and stamina.

THE FLIGHT OF THE DRAGONFLY

The two subspecies of dragonfly can be distinguished by their flights. That of the Zygoptera is slow and clumsy since the front and rear wings do not beat together. Anisoptera, on the other hand, are much more coordinated and their wings beat in perfect harmony.

Certain dragonflies keep their wings spread when resting since neither the front nor rear set can be folded away. Males often damage their wings defending their territory which makes flying more difficult.

A dragonfly's body is made up of head, thorax and abdomen. The shape of the thorax, on which the wings and the last two pairs of legs are located, gives the insect its power in the air.

The wings of the blue aeshna, one of the 88 known species of anisoptera in Europe, are transparent in the male and slightly coloured in the female. The back wings are a little larger than the front. Each pair operates independently and is controlled by powerful muscles attached directly to the base of the wings.

QUICK AND AGILE

The dragonfly's diet is made up of dipterous insects, e.g. mosquitoes and mayflies. It has no problem locating its prey thanks to its large eyes and the flexibility of its head. With great agility, it flies after its prey before catching it. A dragonfly is capable of maintaining a speed of around four to nine metres a second (equivalent to twenty wing beats) for several hours. Due to the structure of their nervous system, *Anisoptera* are able to coordinate their wing movements, making their flight extremely graceful. The rhythm of these movements is only altered when the insect wants to change direction or perform different manoeuvres. The

slight buzzing sound that you hear when they fly by is made by the edge of their wings. Some birds, such as hoobies and kestrels, are able to catch dragonflies in mid-flight. The dragonfly's main asset when it comes to escaping from predators is not so much its speed, which is never more than 25 kilometres per hour, but its agility, being able to change direction quickly and easily.

Dragonflies often land on the ground, on moss at the edge of water or forest tracks.
The position of their legs makes it very difficult for them to walk along the ground.
They can, however, climb up objects, such as rushes and moss, in order to lay their eggs.

Too heavy to fly, **ostriches** are champion runners

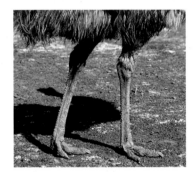

An ostrich can stride up to 3.5 metres.

The ostrich has extremely muscular legs. It is the only bird with feet that consist of two toes. The toe that points inwards is larger than the other and has a thick nail that can be used as a weapon against predators.

THE LEGS OF AN ATHLETE

Along with the rhea of South America, the emu and cassowary of Australia, and the kiwi of New Zealand, the ostrich of Africa forms the family of Ratitae. It is able to move very quickly because of the length and strength of its legs and the way in which its feet are formed. The ostrich can easily maintain a speed of between 30 and 50 kilometres per hour for up to half an hour. In an emergency, it can even reach speeds of up to 70 kilometres per hour, equivalent to 20 metres a second. This means it is capable of running the 100 metres in just five seconds! A strong runner, the ostrich is also capable of jumping heights of up to 1.5 metres.

Outside the mating season, the ostrich spends most of its time looking for food. It often lives a nomadic existence, covering anything between 10 and 40 kilometres a day to find the plants and water that it needs. It nearly always moves around as part of a group, pecking at anything en route.

Distribution
of the ostrich

In the past, the ostrich was found throughout the savannahs and semi-desert regions of Africa. Today, however, its numbers have dropped significantly, particularly in the northern parts of Africa and especially since the end of the 19th century.

In September, during the mating season, fights may break out between two males over a female. The two rivals take part in what is actually a pretend fight. Several males may become involved in a battle at the same time, each hoping to frighten off the others by spreading its wings to make itself look like the biggest and most threatening.

Famous for being slow,
garden snails
actually carry their houses around at 50 metres per hour

The snail moves by crawling along on a large muscular foot, situated on its stomach. It is from this method of locomotion that the term gastropod, of which the snail is an example, comes. The literal meaning of 'gastropod' is having the stomach in the foot. This foot secretes a sticky liquid or slime that aids movement and leaves behind a shiny trail.

THE FORMULA 1 OF THE SNAIL WORLD

The garden snail is grey in colour and a land mollusc that belongs to the class of Gastropoda. Whilst other snails have difficulty reaching speeds of 58 centimetres per hour, the garden snail has a top speed of 50 metres per hour, or around 80 centimetres a minute. This performance makes it the fastest of the slow, at almost a hundred times faster than other snails. Like all snails, the garden snail does not like the sun, which causes it to dehydrate, and prefers to go out in the rain. When in danger, the shell that it carries on its back serves as a shelter.

The garden snail belongs to the family of Helicidae which probably includes several thousand different species, all of which are similar enough to be given the general term of snail. Many types of snail are sought after as food and have been since Roman times when they were bred in huge quantities.

Given that it is extremely prone to dehydration, the snail is particularly attracted to damp ground and bushes, preferring to go out in the rain. In spring, the animal is forced to make up for the liquid that it has lost during hibernation.

Situated underneath the snail, the animal's T-shaped mouth consists of a horny jaw and a rasping tongue, known as a 'radula'. It is with the help of these organs that the animal eats leaves. The head is clearly differentiated from the body and has two large tentacles, bearing its eyes, and two smaller tentacles, used for feeling.

Formidable warriors, **cheetahs** are the fastest mammals on earth

A CAT BORN TO RUN

Related to the panther, the cheetah likes nothing more than to run through long grass. Its name comes for the Sanskrit 'citrakaya' meaning 'bright speckled body'. Its suppleness and build are ideally suited to running, and hunting. Cheetahs are small enough to reach high speeds and heavy enough to catch and kill its prey. Everything about its body shows it was designed for speed: the length of its legs, body and tail as well as the depth of its chest. It is capable of reaching speeds of up to 115 kilometres per hour.

The cheetah's backbone is so flexible that it enables it to 'fly' half of the time. Like the horse, its four feet leave the ground completely as it brings them together. Furthermore, all four feet leave the ground again when the legs are extended, something that the horse is not capable of doing. The cheetah's suppleness also enables it to turn as quickly as the gazelle, one of its favourite prey.

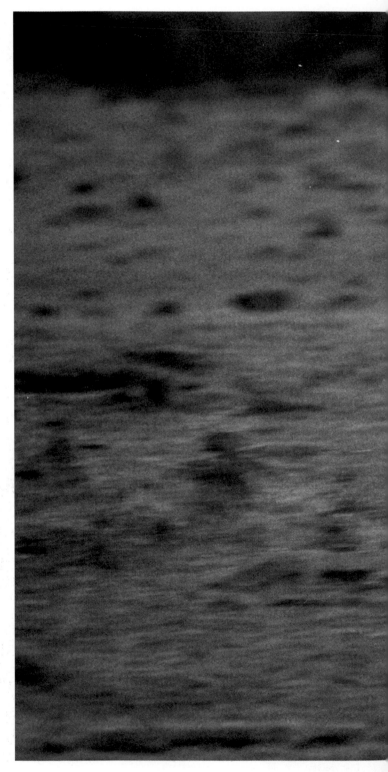

Whilst almost extinct in Asia, cheetahs are still present in Africa. Their survival is precarious in the west, more stable in the south. In the Kruger National Park, in South Africa, cheetahs live in more wooded areas than the Savannah in which they are usually found.

Historic distribution

Present-day distribution

The cheetah's large muscles enable it to accelerate suddenly: it can increase from 0 to 75 kilometres per hour in just 2 seconds. The animal is, however, not able to maintain this effort over long distances as it would risk brain damage due to lack of oxygen.

The cheetah's head is proportionally smaller than that of other cats. This disproportion adds to the impression of it being a graceful animal. Its canine teeth are not very large which enables it to breathe in air more easily. A distinct advantage when running!

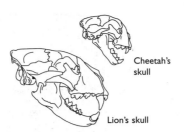

Cheetah's skull

Lion's skull

The cheetah is able to cross the wide open spaces that it inhabits at great speed but also seems to enjoy climbing, scaling a fallen trunk or perching on the fork of a tree. The animal uses its claws to mark these tree trunks, issuing a visual warning to other cheetahs to stay away.

COHABITATION IN THE SAVANNAH

The cheetah's canine teeth are very short and thin.

The cheetah spends the time that it is not hunting for food marking out its territory. Each animal systematically visits a number of strategic points on its route in order to find out the identity of the area's owner. This enables it to avoid being surprised by a potential enemy. Like all members of the cat family, the cheetah marks out its territory with a stream of urine.

The cheetah shares the slightly wooded areas of the African savannah with the lion and the panther, but it has been less successful than the others at adapting to the presence of humans. It chooses different prey to the other two, preferring to hunt during the day, unlike the lion, and in the open, unlike the panther that lies in wait for its prey. These differences enable the three predators to cohabit, even if lions and panthers are a constant threat to young cheetahs.

Raising cubs is a difficult time for the female. On the one hand, she needs more food in order to feed them properly. On the other hand, she is not able to move around as freely. At first, she refuses to leave her young, carrying them around in her mouth if they are unable to follow. In spite of the care she takes, only about one in three lives to become an adult.

As it flies past, the cheetah is a picture of gracefulness.

A THREATENED SPECIES?

There are only two subspecies of cheetah, classified according to their distribution: the African cheetah *Acinonyx jubatus jubatus*, and the Asian cheetah *Acinonyx jubatus venaticus*.

Some specialists claim that the cheetah is not under threat of extinction, unlike the panther which is said to be the more threatened of the two in spite of all its supposed skills of adaptation. The unobtrusive nature of the cheetah, causing it to shy away from areas inhabited by man has made it less susceptible than the lion and the panther to the wrath of farmers.

According to others, the cheetah is now a species under the threat of extinction. It seems to have disappeared from Asia where it could still be found at the beginning of this century. The last cheetah to be spotted in India was back in 1948. One night, a hunter killed three male cheetahs that he found together. Since then, none have ever been seen.

The last remaining cheetahs in the Middle East are to be found in Iran where there are estimated to be around 250. In Arabia, its presence is not confirmed, but there are still rumours of a number of alleged sightings.

Their numbers remain stable in eastern and southern parts of Africa. Elsewhere in western areas, in the Sahel and on the edges of the Sahara, the situation is deteriorating rapidly. The total population in Africa is now estimated at 25,000.

Like a coil, the cheetah leaps after its prey in the African savannah, seemingly flying over the ground. It can reach up to speeds of 100 kilometres per hour in just a few seconds.

Profile

Cheetah
Acinonyx jubatus
Family: Felidae
Size: 1.12 m – 1.5 m for the body; 0.7 m – 0.9 m to the withers
Weight: 35 kg – 70 kg
Habitat: dry savannahs, grassy plains and occasionally wooded savannahs
Diet: strict carnivore
Gestation period: 90 – 95 days
Number of young per brood: 3 – 4
Life expectancy: 3 – 4 years
Distinguishing features: the cheetah does not mate well in captivity

HUGE TERRITORIES

In areas where there is a large concentration of cheetahs, the animals mark out their territory. If one animal comes across a mark that has been left by another within the past 24 hours, it will take the opposite direction. This avoids too many animals hunting in the same area. In order to survive, a cheetah needs a territory that covers between 50 and 150 square kilometres. Within this area, the male will cover around 7 kilometres daily and the female 3.7 kilometres. The greatest known concentration of cheetahs is found in the Nairobi National Park in Kenya where each animal has a territory of around 5 or 6 square kilometres.

Portrait

The warrior-like behaviour of the cheetah is emphasized further by its speckled coat which enables it to blend into the landscape. The black tear pits that surround its eyes also provide useful camouflage. These two black marks, that continue down the snout of the animal, help it to hide in the long grass of the savannah.

Elsewhere, in more difficult environments, there is something like one animal per 100 or even 250 square kilometres. In extreme cases, such as in the Serengeti where female cheetahs follow the migrations of antelope, hunting grounds can be anything up to 800 square kilometres.

Preferring to hunt by day, the cheetah is without doubt the gazelle's greatest enemy. The speed of the gazelle poses few problems since the cheetah is the fastest carnivore on earth. After a short but effective chase, it throws its prey off balance and knocks it over. It then jumps on the victim, grabbing it by the throat and killing it. Using its canine teeth, it tears the meat up and eats it.

Covering huge distances, **teals** head south for the winter

THE SMALLEST WILD DUCK

The common teal looks like a dwarf next to the other European species of wild duck. An extremely timid bird, it is frequently found on small lakes and ponds surrounded by reeds. There is one European and two North American subspecies.

The common teal covers huge distances, migrating south for the winter. Like the shelduck and the mallard, it is a member of the Anatidae family (ducks) and is an agile bird that can reach speeds of up to 120 kilometres per hour in the air.

Thanks to its long pointed wings, the teal can take to the air from the surface of water without a run-up. After being in the water, however, it must beat its wing energetically in order to shake off all the drops clinging to its feathers.

Profile

La sarcelle
Anas crecca
Family: Anatidae (ducks)
Weight: 250 g – 450 g

Habitat: ponds and lakes, in Europe and North America
Diet: aquatic plants
Incubation period: 23 days
Number of eggs per brood: 5 – 6
Predators: hunters (the green-winged teal is the second most hunted duck in North America after the mallard)
Distinguishing features: teals migrate in flocks of several hundred birds.

Like the swan and the goose, the teal is a member of the Anatidae family. The feathers of these birds must constantly be coated with grease to protect them when swimming.

A paddler or a diver?

The family of Anatidae can be divided into those ducks that dive and those that feed on the surface. The teal belongs to the second group, diving only when forced to and rarely more than a metre below the surface. It brings its food, which consists mainly of plants, to the surface of the water by simply paddling!

OUR NORTH AMERICAN COUSIN

The green-winged teal, a cousin of our common teal, is found in Canada, Alaska, Maine, North Dakota and northern parts of Michigan. Each year it flies south to spend winter in south-western parts of the United States and Mexico. Weighing between 250 and 450 grams, the teal is the smallest surface feeding duck in America. It lives off small aquatic animals and plants which it finds in abundance in shallow waters near the bank or in waterholes. When they are not splashing around in water, teals are fast and agile flyers and are the only ducks that can scratch themselves while flying! They do not dive in order to hunt for food, but they have been known to dive under water to escape from predators. They sleep standing up with their beak tucked under their black feathers and preen themselves by shaking, stretching out and pecking at their feathers.

Like other species of duck, the teal can be identified by a 'speculum', a bright patch of feathers on its wings. This patch is made up of metallic markings on most types of surface feeding duck, of which the teal is one. These striking 'mirrors' act as signals to other birds in the group, helping them to stay together when flying.

Between mudbaths, **warthogs**
trot around the savannah at a remarkable speed

The warthog is the only member of the Suidae family to walk on its wrists whilst searching for food. As a result of this strange method of locomotion, large protective calluses have formed on these joints.

AN ODD-LOOKING CREATURE

Like other members of the Suidae family, the warthog and its cousin, the European wild boar, are not noted for their beauty. The warthog has a barrel-shaped body, a large and heavy head covered with strange wart-like growths and enormous canine teeth. Its skin and fur are black.

The warthog can move at an amazing 55 kilometres per hour, equivalent to running the 100 metres in less than 7 seconds! Its sight is quite poor, but its eyes, which are placed high and to the back of its head, give it a wide range of vision even when it is grazing with its head down. It has highly developed senses of smell and hearing.

When warthogs break into a trot, their tail goes up as a signal of their presence. Being vegetarians, they are not normally aggressive animals. Having said that, males frequently take part in fights and sparring matches when the wart-like growths covering their head are used to cushion blows, whilst also serving as anti-slip devices.

Warthogs love rolling in the mud!

THE AFRICAN COUSIN OF THE BOAR

The warthog, also known as the savannah boar, is native to Africa. It is found in the savannah, always close to water where it can drink and roll in the mud.

Hunted for its meat, the species is extremely common south of the Sahara, except in South Africa where it is almost extinct. There is also another species known as the Cape or desert warthog which is found in Kenya and Somalia.

The warthog protects itself from predators by burying itself in natural holes or those dug by the aardvark. Unlike other wild hogs, it is active during the day but can become nocturnal if hunted by man. Warthogs live in groups of four to six animals, often sharing territories with other groups. Although they do not keep to one particular territory, there can be competition between different groups, fighting over food and watering holes.

Huge canine teeth

The warthog has upper canine teeth that can reach 25 to 63 centimetres in length in males, and 15 to 25 centimetres in females. The shape of its teeth is linked to its diet. It lives mainly off grasses which it crushes with its lower canines. These pointed teeth are like razors and are sharpened as they rub against the other teeth.

Profile

Warthog
Phacochoerus africanus
Family: Suidae
Size: 90 – 150 cm
Weight: 50 – 150 kg

Distribution: Africa, south of the Sahara: Ghana, Somalia and South Africa
Habitat: savannahs, light bush and grass plains
Diet: grasses (Gramineae)
Gestation period: 170 – 175 days
Number of young per brood: 1 – 8
Life expectancy: 10 – 12 years
Predators: man who hunts it for its tusks and meat

Unlike other Suidae, the female warthog leaves her young alone during the day. She leaves them in the morning and returns around midday to feed them.

Scurrying along at top speed,
centipedes
look as though they have a hundred legs

CHAMPIONS OF THE MULTI-LEGGED RACE

Classed for many years as myriapods or millipedes, chilopods are those insects that are often agile with long bodies divided into a head and trunk. The number of pairs of legs varies from 15 to more than 171. Strangely enough, the number is always odd. The term 'millipede' is therefore a slight exaggeration. The stone centipede (Lithobius) and the house centipede (Scutigera), members of the Chilopoda, have only fifteen pairs of legs when fully grown. These are, however, used to maximum effect, enabling them to move quickly along the ground.

The stone centipede is the most common species in Europe. The body of the insect is brown and usually measures 2 to 3 centimetres in length, but can reach 4.5 centimetres. It lives under stones and the bark of trees, feeding mainly on slugs and small insects.

The house centipede is very similar to the stone centipede and is distinguishable by its legs and antennae which are much longer.

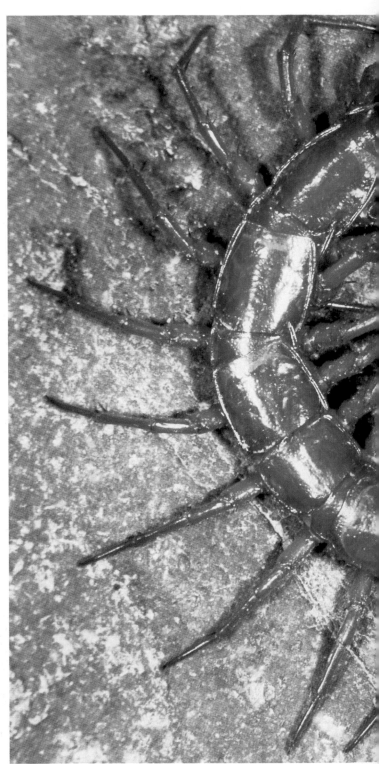

Chilopoda are instantly recognizable by the shape of their powerful jaw-like claws. The poisonous pincers are used by these carnivorous insects to kill their prey.

The antennae of a stone centipede contain the organs which enable it to find its prey without which it would starve to death. The last two pairs of legs of the stone centipede are known as 'trailing legs' as they are slightly longer than the others'. Not that this prevents the insect from moving with amazing speed.

House centipedes are predators that move with such speed that it is often difficult for the naked eye to see them when they begin scurrying. They are frequently found in homes and can often be seen running up walls at night in search of their prey, mainly mosquitoes and other insects.

With its long antennae, made up of over 400 joints, and its long thin legs, the house centipede is like an ultra-light ghostly apparition. Unjustly persecuted by humans, whose homes it inhabits, it hides during the day in dark corners and hunts at night, rapidly killing its prey with the venom in its jaw-like claws.

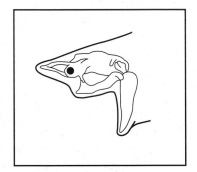

The behaviour of blue sharks towards divers is unpredictable.

With their tapered body,
blue sharks
are excellent swimmers

POWER AND SPEED

The blue shark belongs to the group of animals known as 'man-eaters'. Its body is powerful and slender, its tail incredibly long. It is a fish of the open sea that rarely attacks swimmers. The blue shark is found in tropical, sub-tropical and temperate regions of all the world's oceans. In Europe it is common in the Mediterranean, but rare in the North Sea. In the eastern Pacific, it is found from the Gulf of Alaska to the waters off the coast of Chile. The fish lives anywhere between the surface and a depth of 152 metres. It migrates vast distances and is an excellent swimmer, reaching speeds of up to 70 kilometres per hour. When the temperature of the water rises in summer, sharks migrate north, returning south in winter.

The mouth of a shark consists of an upper jaw and a lower jaw, or mandible. The upper jaw is not part of the skull but is attached to it by ligaments, enabling the shark to open its mouth wider.

The spindle-shaped, or fusiform, body of the blue shark encounter little resistance as it moves through the water. Its body, which tapers at both ends, cuts through the water which then converges behind it along its elongated tail. This narrow slender shape enables many fish, including tuna, to reach high speeds in water.

The blue shark benefits from natural camouflage. Its powerful muscular body is darker on the top than underneath. When the animal swims below a diver, its dark back cannot be seen against the bottom of the ocean. When it swims above, its light underside blends in with the light coming from the surface.

In spite of their fragile appearance, **greyhounds** are sprinters with muscles of steel

The town of Palm Beach, in Florida, is famous for its greyhound races which attract crowds of people.

AN ANCIENT EGYPTIAN GOD

The greyhound is a species from which most domesticated dogs are descended. Its picture has been found in cave paintings dating back some 8000 years. In Egypt, the ancestor of the modern greyhound was considered to be a god by the Egyptians and its image is often found on the walls of royal tombs.

THE ENGLISHMAN'S RACING DOG

The greyhound is the result of breeding by the British, looking to create a dog that was brave and fast. It is believed to have been brought to the West by the Phoenicians, then chosen during the time of Henry VIII for the hunting of hares, or coursing. Today, the tough but elegant greyhound is trained to take part in races.

Bred from highly developed hunting dogs, greyhounds owe their fur and colour to the cross-breeding of mastiffs and sheepdogs. The large English greyhound has a short smooth firm coat of no one particular colour. Males weigh between 29 and 32 kilograms, females between 27 and 29 kilograms. It is highly valued by the English as a racing dog, as is the smaller English greyhound, or whippet. On the racetrack, a greyhound can reach speeds of up to 60 kilometres per hour.

The greyhound is the main race dog in Britain, and greyhound racing is also very popular in the United States, notably in Florida. But this champion was known for its speed long before it conquered the West – Cleopatra is said to have owned greyhounds trained for racing.

Greyhounds have a slender body, long legs, erect ears, a deep chest and an arched back.

The dogs are trained to run after big bones.

THE AMERICAN'S TOO!

Much enjoyed by the British, greyhound racing is also very popular in America. The competitions organized on the west coast attract a large and enthusiastic public. The town Palm Beach in Florida, once famous for its wonderful beaches of soft sand is now associated with greyhound racing. This sport fits in perfectly with the fashionable and elegant atmosphere of the town.

END OF AN ATHLETE CAREER

As competition athletes, greyhounds undergo very intensive training very early in their lives. Once its career is over, a retired dog, still relatively young, is usually adopted by a family.

The greyhound is not only a proven sportsman, it is also a skilful hunting dog, due to its sharp eyesight. As hunting dogs, they cooperate with other species and spontaneously create their own hunting strategies during beating. This skill has resulted in them featuring on many tapestries depicting hunting scenes.

The symbol of Australia,
kangaroos
jump like jack-in-the-boxes on their hind legs

During the early part of its life, the young kangaroo, or joey, takes shelter in its mother's pouch at the slightest hint of danger.

IT'S IN THE BAG!

The kangaroo belongs to the family of Macropodidae, meaning 'that which has big feet', which consists of 50 species, all of whom are only found on the islands of the central and south Pacific. Its main physical characteristics that contribute to its particular ability to jump, are a large muscular tail and hind legs that are much longer than those at the front. It is also a marsupial which means a mammal without a placenta. The female has a pocket, or pouch, known as a 'marsupium', in which the young kangaroo develops.

The kangaroo's jump

In what is always a spectacular sight, the animal advances at speed by jumping. It uses its hind legs like a spring, moving its head and front legs forwards and using its tail as a balance. Continuing in this way by a series of successive jumps, it can reach speeds of up to 40 kilometres an hour, or 11 metres a second.

Although they are essentially placid animals, male kangaroos sometimes fight over a female. They begin by staring each other out, raising up on their hind legs, and then punching each other with their two hands.

Studies have shown that kangaroos use up less energy when jumping quickly than when they move along with smaller jumps at less than 18 kilometres an hour.

While resting, kangaroos stand on all fours.

Powerful hind legs

The kangaroo's hind legs are extremely powerful and muscular, enabling it to stand on them. They are particularly suited to jumping, given the elasticity of the muscle, and are an equally formidable, and often lethal weapon. The tail, which is equally powerful and muscular, serves as a third foot when resting, and a balance when jumping.

HOP, SKIP AND A JUMP!

The kangaroo is capable of jumping 3 metres in height and 9 metres in length. It only achieves these distances, however, when fleeing from a predator over open countryside. When looking for a watering hole or another kangaroo, its jumps do not exceed 1.9 metre in length, enabling it to travel at a speed of around 20 kilometres per hour, bouncing off the ground like a spring. As soon as it feels threatened, however, the kangaroo will increase its speed in order to escape danger.

The kangaroo's jump consists of four stages. During the first stage, it releases its back legs like a spring, forming an angle of 45° with the ground. Next, it throws its head and front legs forwards into an almost horizontal position, bringing its tail into line with the rest of its body. As it lands, it moves its tail sharply upwards so that it does not hit the ground.

In areas of grassy plains and semi-arid savannahs, the grass is often yellow during periods of drought that can last several months. When the drought is severe, kangaroos are capable of covering dozens of kilometres in search of areas where there is more food and where the climate is more suited to mating.

In trees and on the ground,
black mambas and sand boas
slither along dangerously...quick

The black mamba (*Dendroaspis polylepis*) is a large thin tree snake with a long narrow head, smooth scales arranged diagonally, and large eyes with round pupils. The large teeth along its lower jaw are used to hold on to its prey along with the fangs of the upper jaw. Generally olive-brown or grey-brown in colour, it often comes down to the ground.

THE BLACK MAMBA: ELEGANT AND VIOLENT

The black mamba is the largest poisonous snake in Africa. Its sudden reactions as well as its elegant and rapid movements are always impressive. It is also the fastest snake on land, reaching speeds of up to 3 metres per second over short distances.

THE BOA THAT BURIES ITSELF IN SAND

The sand boa is a small snake that lives in dry or desert areas where it can quickly bury itself in loose ground or sand. It comes out at night to hunt for rodents.

The black mamba lives in the savannah and dry tropical forests. Elegant and quick, it is highly unpredictable and is one of the world's most feared snakes because of its lethal venom. Considered to be the longest poisonous snake in the world, after the king cobra, it averages 3m, but can grow to a length of 4.5 metres.

The sand boa (Eryx colubrinus) is a small snake of less than a metre in length, with a head covered in small scales that is not distinct from its body. Its back is reddy-brown in colour or a dark brown mottled with yellow or orange. Unlike other boas, it is found in the driest and sandiest semi-desert regions, living under the top layer of sand.

Performing aerial acrobatics,
peregrine falcons
are the fastest birds in the world

The peregrine falcon spends many an hour on lookout duty, sometimes on a branch, watching for intruders onto its territory.

NOSEDIVING AT 360 KM/H

The Falconidae are a family of birds of prey that are ideally suited to hunting in the air over long distances. The peregrine falcon is a worthy representative of this family. Living up to its nickname of 'master of the skies', it is capable of spectacular acrobatics and incredible speeds, and is easily the fastest bird in the world. It reaches its maximum speed during nosedives, a technique used only for hunting. During the course of one of these dives, it can reach speeds of up to 360 kilometres per hour.

Piercing eyes

The peregrine falcon has excellent vision. Its piercing eyes enable it to spot its prey from a distance of one and a half kilometres, and thus see without being seen. They are protected by prominent eyebrow arches which lend the bird a fierce and proud air.

This peregrine falcon has just caught a rock dove. It strips the feathers from its victim before beginning the feast, starting with the brain and muscles. The meal lasts between 10 and 30 minutes on average .

When they hatch, the chicks are covered with white down which lasts several weeks. This down is not thick enough to protect them from the cold, so their mother must keep them warm.

A SKILLED HUNTER

The peregrine falcon is particularly skilled at catching other birds in mid-flight, making the most of its two main assets: piercing vision and speed. Both these qualities enable it to surprise its prey. It has two different strategies: either it attacks its prey by straddling it, or dives and crashes into it at great speed, gripping the victim with its rear talons.

MASTER OF THE SKIES

Everything about the physique of the peregrine

A falcon soars high above its territory.

falcon is geared towards becoming 'master of the skies'. When spread, its narrow pointed wings give it a triangular shape. Its long legs, on the other hand, are covered down to its heels with large feathers called 'pants' which conceal them and make the bird itself more streamlined in the air.

The peregrine falcon soars effortlessly high above the ground making the most of thermal currents. By doing this, it can rise to several hundred metres above its territory without wasting energy. A veritable gliding champion, it increases its lift by spreading its wing and tail feathers (which it keeps tightly folded in other types of flight).

The fastest
spiders
cover 53 cm in a second

On the edge of the spiders web lies a sort of woven bag which is where it lives. A number of threads are arranged over the surface of the web in a way that trips up insects and makes it extremely difficult for them to walk over it.

Profile

House spider
Tegeneria domestica
Family: Agelenidae

Size: 12 – 18 mm
Habitat: homes and gardens in Europe and North America
Diet: insects
Predators: other spiders, birds
One week after fertilization, the female lays eggs which hatch several weeks later
Distinguishing features: spiders are sensitive to vibrations, especially those of a low frequency, as sent out by the prey captured in their webs.

A LAND SPEED RECORD

Among the Arachnidae (spiders, scorpions, acarids...), the record for the fastest over a flat surface is held by the Tegenaria spider, related to the house spiders that we find in our cellars and attics. The Tegenaria has reached speeds of up to 53 centimetres per second (or 1.8 kilometres per hour) which is equivalent to 33 times the length of its own body per second. By way of comparison, humans can only manage 5.5 times their own height per second. In order to match this performance, they would have to run at 207 kilometres per hour!

All spiders have one pair of appendages that they use for feeding and four pairs that are used for walking, as well as a silk gland which is located on the under side of their abdomen.

There are 35,000 known species of spider in the world. The house spider spins threads known as 'trip lines', whilst other species spin sticky webs to trap their prey.

The house spider belongs to a group known as chelicerates which owe their name to a pair of small pincers located in front of their mouth, known as chelicerae. These appendages are used for catching and keeping hold of prey, notably insects. They are connected to a poison gland containing venom that is capable of paralysing the victim. The venom also helps with the external digestion of its food.

In spite of its small size, the Shetland pony has great stamina.

Trained to race,
horses
were born to run

STRONG AND FAST

Like the ass and the zebra, its cousins in the Equidae family, the horse's foot consists of one toe protected by a horny hoof. Its slender legs and strong physique make it ideally suited to running. Racehorses travel at a top speed of 60 kilometres per hour, reaching 66 kilometres per hour over short distances of around a hundred metres. English thoroughbreds, chosen for their speed and stamina, can even reach speeds of up to 70 kilometres per hour. As for Arabian horses, they are able to travel at 18 kilometres per hour over distances of 100 to 150 kilometres. Furthermore, the horse can pull up to 77 percent of its own body weight.

Horsepower

It is in horsepower (HP) that the power of an internal combustion engine is measured. One horsepower represents the power needed to lift a weight of 75 kilograms one metre in one second. For such a short period of time, the horse can in fact perform better; a good jumping horse can clear eight metres. Light horses can pull 77 percent of their own body weight, and larger individuals, 68 percent.

The Arabian thoroughbred is a lively animal with big eyes and a saddle horse that is both graceful and full of stamina. Along with the English thoroughbred it has sired the Anglo-Arabian, the finest of all saddle horses. According to legend, this horse was first bred by Allah. This graceful horse is the object of much praise. Easy to train, it is said to be its rider's partner rather than simply their mount.

The Anglo-Arabian is the result of crossbreeding between English and Arabian thoroughbreds and is extremely popular as a saddle horse. A graceful and spirited runner, it is said to reach speeds of up to 70 kilometres per hour. Here, the horse has been caught in mid-gallop across a field. Its four feet are gathered together underneath it and none of them is touching the ground.

After years of using a simple rope to stop a horse, man finally learned to take advantage of the sensitivity of the animal's gums, inventing the bit which is placed in its mouth.

The horse moves on a single digit at the end of fused bones. Like all Equidae, it has a single horny hoof covering the final section of its third toe, the only one that is fully formed.

Profile

The horse
Equus caballus
Family: Equidae
Size to withers: 1.47 m (pony) – 1.8 m (shire horse)
Habitat: domesticated species, all continents; wild species, North America, Australia, the Camargue (southern France)
Diet: strict herbivore
Gestation period: 10 – 12 months
Number of young per brood: 1 foal
Distinguishing features: no rutting season; foals are born all year round

RUNNING IN FOUR-FOUR TIME

Galloping is the term given to the fastest speed of Equidae, coming after trotting and cantering. It is whilst galloping that the horse, and in particular the racehorse, can reach incredible speeds. A distinction is drawn between the gathered gallop, in which there are three beats, and the stretched gallop, in which there are four. In the gathered gallop, the horse moves its left hind leg forward and places it on the ground, then moves its right hind leg forward at the same time as its left foreleg, and finally brings its right foreleg down. It leaves the ground, pushing off on its right foreleg whilst the other three gather together beneath it. This is known as a 'right gallop'. In a 'left gallop', the horse first moves its right hind leg forward. In the stretched gallop, the horse advances at the same rhythm, but strides out to reach its top speed. During the fourth beat of the stretched gallop, the horse, carried along by its own momentum, is actually 'suspended' above the ground.

Trotting is the most natural speed for a horse to travel at. The animal moves opposite front and hind legs alternatively, without touching the ground between the two movements.

Harness races are very popular in France and the United States. In Russia famous trotting horses, such as the Orlov, are bred. The quality of these breeds improves each year.

The Arabian thoroughbred was picked from the plains of northern Arabia. Its physical and aesthetic qualities soon led it to be introduced on to other continents where it was used to improve the local breeds. The foal sticks close to its mother for the first few days after it is born, feeding from her for around ten months.

Arabian horses were first brought to Europe during the time of the Crusades. At that time, they were used to improve local breeds. The Arabian horse has a long body: it measures between 1.35 metres and 1.5 metres to its withers. Its coat is short, allowing its muscles and veins to be seen through its thin skin. In Europe, these animals are best suited to the warm climate of the Mediterranean.

With the agility of a cat,
ring-tailed lemurs
perform some amazing jumps

The lemur is able to stand up on its two hind legs and can cover several metres in this position.

A PRIMATE THAT JUMPS LIKE A CAT

The ring-tailed lemur lives in the southern parts of the island of Madagascar in the Indian Ocean. It belongs to the Lemuridae family, a group of prosimian primates. This agile climber of exceptional balance moves fearlessly from tree to tree. It is capable of crossing a two-metre gap between two trees in around a second. It can also perform amazing leaps of five or six metres between vertical and horizontal branches. Its tail, stretched out horizontally at the moment of take-off, acts as a balance.

A jump of two metres

As it begins its leap from one branch to another, the lemur lifts its long tail, with its forelegs outstretched and its hands raised. In the middle of the jump, its tail drops and its hind legs bend to soften the force of landing. This leap of two metres takes only a second. Not bad, eh?

Both young and adult ring-tailed lemurs love to curl up with each other, purring with pleasure like cats. After it is born, the young lemur remains clinging to its mother's chest for several days.

The thick tail of the ring-tailed lemur is marked with fourteen rings of white fur. It is as long as the rest of its body, reaching up to 50 centimetres in length, but cannot be used for holding on.

The ring-tailed lemur is a threatened species in Madagascar since its natural habitat, the forest, has been partly destroyed by humans for wood and farming. This extensive deforestation is a threat to the survival of a species that is supposedly protected.

Lemurs learn to jump form an early age, sometimes using the tail of an adult to steady themselves. These leaps can reach up to 5 or even 6 metres. The tail, which is lifted up at the beginning of the jump, lowered during the middle part and held horizontally on landing, acts as a balance. The animal itself bends double and flexes its knees to land.

The lobster has ten legs, of which the front pair are modified as powerful pincers. These pincers are veritable tools of survival, with one used as a hammer for grinding and the other used as scissors for cutting.

Lobsters and crayfish
do the backstroke to flee

EVERYBODY BACK!

Crustaceans have one pair of broad legs like leaves which, along with the end part of the abdomen, forms a fan known as the 'tail fan'. This fan enables them to move backwards at speed by folding the abdomen violently and beating the water in a jerking manner. This ability to swim backwards at speed proves extremely useful when trying to escape from danger. The lobster *Homarus vulgaris* and the spiny lobster, or crayfish, *Palinurus vulgaris* are able to travel at 23 kilometres per hour using this stroke, equivalent to ten times the length of their body in a second!

Profile

The lobster
Homarus vulgaris
Size: 45 – 60 cm in length, excluding the pincers
Weight: up to 9 kg

Family: Homaridae
Habitat: rocky, muddy or sandy environments, between 0 and 120 m below the surface
Diet: crabs, molluscs, worms, sea urchins, starfish, fish, seaweed
Number of eggs per brood: 5000 – 50,000
Life expectancy: 50 years and over

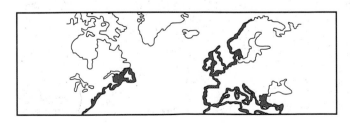

The red spiny lobster spends its days clinging to the walls of underwater caves and rocks around the coasts of the Atlantic, the English Channel, the Mediterranean and the Adriatic Sea.

The spiny lobster, which can grow to a length of 50 centimetres, has a red or dark brown spiny shell. Like all members of the genus *Palinurus*, it does not have pincers.

Accurately speaking, the lobster has three pairs of pincers, but the first set is large enough to distinguish it from other crustaceans. The pincers of the male are extremely large, consisting of a 'hammer' and a 'pair of scissors', making it a fearsome predator.

The lobster's shell is generally dark blue, speckled with white, providing the animal with a strong protective cover. The shell can also be pale blue in colour, and more rarely, a yellow white. A wider range of colours are found when the animal is farmed. Outside the shedding period, which happens about once a year, the adult has only one predator: man.

Moving like lightning
Squirrels
jumps from tree to tree

ACROBATICS IN THE TREES

With its long bushy tail, its superb reddish brown coat and its large mischievous eyes, the red squirrel is one of the most common animals in European forests. It is an excellent climber and jumper, scaling tree trunks with the help of the sharp claws at the end of its toes. It also performs perilous acrobatics, using its tail to guide it. In addition to this, the squirrel is also as quick as lightning, capable of some impressive jumps thanks to the powerful spring of its long hind legs. During these jumps, it arches its tail to maintain its balance and uses its claws to grab hold of the bark.

Having spent its whole life in trees, the red squirrel can move gracefully from branch to branch. With strong eyesight and a wide field of vision, it is always on the alert. Even when it comes down to the ground, it is always on the lookout knowing that a predator could arrive at any moment!

Profile

The red squirrel
Sciurus vulgaris
Family: Sciuridae (rodents)
Size: 20 – 25 cm for its head and body; 15 – 20 cm for its tail
Weight: 230 – 480 g
Habitat: conifers and broad-leaved trees
Diet: seeds
Predators: birds of prey (owls, goshawks), carnivores (martens)
Gestation period: 38 – 39 days
Number of young per brood: 3 – 5
Life expectancy: around 12 years
Distinguishing features: its long tail is thick and bushy, especially in winter

The red squirrel inhabits the woodlands of Eurasia and the taiga of Russia. It is also found in European forests where conifers and broad-leaved trees grow. In mountain areas, it is not so much the cold as the lack of trees that limits its numbers.

Perching on the end of a branch, this squirrel prepares to jump. With its claws digging into the bark and its tail up, it first judges the distance it has to cover. Then, with a sudden push from its very long hind legs, particularly suited to life among the trees, it throws itself into the air. During the jump, it changes direction using its tail which acts as a type of rudder.

FOND OF PINE CONES

The red squirrel likes to live close to coniferous forests where it finds most of its food. A large part of its diet is made up of seeds, such as those found at the base of pine cones. Such is its love of this food that it will move to find the area where this fruit is in season. For this reason, a poor crop of cones can lead to massive migrations, especially by young animals, covering many kilometres.

A VARIED DIET

The squirrel's diet is, however, not just limited to pine cones. It also knows how to make the most of what each season brings. It will therefore eat branches and shoots in spring, gnawing away at the bark of young trees. In summer, it hunts for fruit in the forest, be it berries or dried fruit. With its sharp teeth, it opens nuts such as almonds to eat the contents. It has also been known to break its diet of seeds and plants to eat small eggs or insects.

With remarkable agility, the red squirrel throws itself into the air to jump from one branch to another. This small swift animal seems to literally fly at times. Its sharp eyes are particularly good at making out vertical shapes, enabling it to judge the distance between trees accurately.

Balancing on a branch with its body outstretched, its tail pointing down and its front legs pointing forwards, the red squirrel reaches for the branch on which it has seen the fruit that it wants. In the quest for food, it is capable of adopting the most amazing positions. Its thumb and four fingers, all with long claws, enable it to get a firm grip.

With scaly wings,
flying fish
pirouette in the foam of the waves

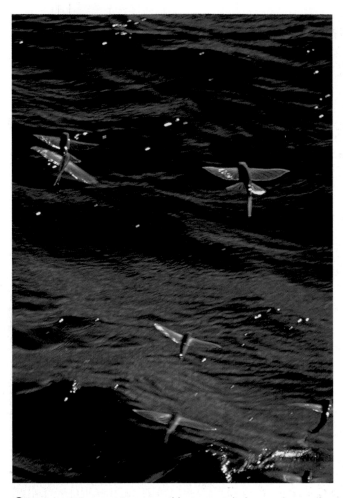

Out at sea, it is sometimes possible to see whole squadrons of several hundred flying fish travelling at speed.

FLYING FISH...

Out at sea, strange flying creatures frequently land on the decks of ships with a loud crash. Sailors are often surprised to discover that the bird in question does not have any feathers, but rather scales and the large bulging eyes of a fish. The creature in question is in fact the flying fish, which at first sight looks like a herring. Its back is bright blue and its silver flanks carry a pair of incredible wing-like pectoral fins. The lower part of its asymmetrical tail is much longer than the upper part, a feature that is very important during 'take-off' and 'landing'.

...OR GLIDING FISH?

For many years it was thought that these fish flew, beating their wings like birds. They do no such thing. Flying fish glide, bouncing off the tops of waves. To lift themselves out of the water, they build up the necessary speed – reaching 55 kilometres per hour – and rise above the surface. At the end of their flight, they fall back towards the water at an angle, and this is when the larger lower part of their tail fin comes into play: by hitting the water with this lobe they are able to gather the necessary speed to rise once more into the air.

Gliding and bouncing

As they grow, flying fish gradually acquire the ability to glide. Their wing-like pectoral fins appear when the young fish measure between 2 and 5 centimetres. By the time they are between 5 and 8 centimetres long, they are already able to leap from 1 to 10 metres. On its first jump, the flying fish can glide for 45 or 50 metres. Thanks to the shape of its tail, it is then able to beat the foam and set off again. By completing three of four successive jumps in this way, the flying fish can cover a distance of 200 metres, at an average height of one metre above the surface of the water. It can, however, sometimes 'fly' higher, jumping into the wind and using the rising air currents generated by the hulls of ships.

If their path is crossed by a ship, flying fish tend to disperse in all directions. Some, however, taken by surprise, can inadvertently 'run aground' on the deck.

The fins of flying fish have such a span that they form an aerofoil enabling the fish to glide for several hundred metres. Some species only have one pair of 'wings'. Others have two pairs. These surface-feeding fish have developed this spectacular method of locomotion in order to catch the insects that they eat.

Creative workshop

*Having studied all of these creatures,
it's time to get creative.*

*All you need are a few odds and ends and a little ingenuity,
and you can incorporate some of the animals we've seen
into beautiful craft objects.*

*These simple projects will give you further insight into the
animal kingdom presented in the pages of this book.*

*An original and simple way to enjoy
the wonderful images of the animal kingdom.*

Kangaroo towel

*T*his friendly marsupial hides a facecloth-puppet in its pouch. You could also use the pouch to keep things in when you are on the beach!

Preparation of the pieces

• Photocopy the designs, increasing them to the desired size.

Cut around the paper designs.

Fold the brown towel in half lengthways and place the middle edge of the kangaroo pattern on the fold. Also place the patterns for the pouch, the facecloth and the ear on to the towel. You will need one pouch piece, two facecloth pieces and four ear pieces. Pin the patterns on to the towel. Cut the kangaroo shape around the outline of the pattern. Cut the other pieces 1 cm larger than their patterns.

Making up the ears

Fold the white fabric in two. Pin the shape of the inside of the ears on the fabric and cut around the pattern. Place the white pieces of material on to the brown ear.

Sew around the white pieces using zigzag stitch.

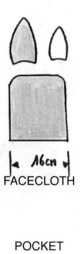

16cm

FACECLOTH

POCKET

18 cm

28cm

Sewing the pocket and the kangaroo

• Stitch a 1-cm seam around all four edges of the pouch. Position the pouch on the kangaroo, and sew along both sides and the bottom.

Sew the kangaroo on to the white towel in the same way that you sewed the ears, using zigzag stitch.

Making up the facecloth

• Take the two pieces of the facecloth, make a hem at the bottom of each piece. Place two ear pieces on to the top of each piece, making sure that the ears with the white pieces are both on the same piece.

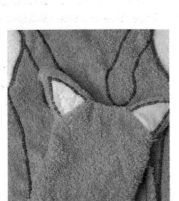

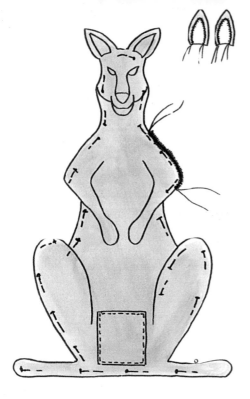

Sew the ears on, then put the two pieces together right sides facing and sew round the sides and the top, including the ears so that when you put your hand inside the 'puppet' your fingers will go into the ears. Turn the puppet the right way round.

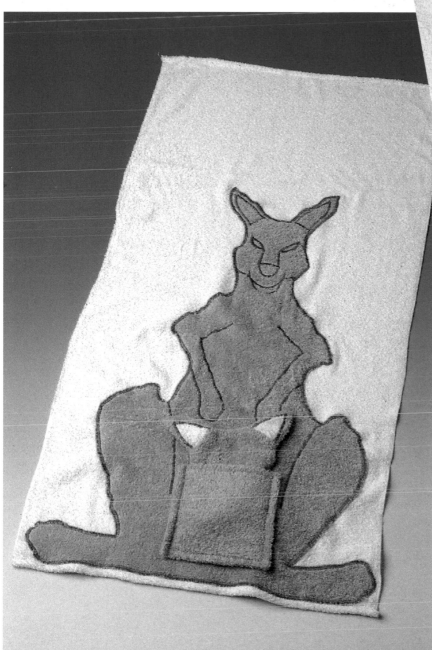

Materials

• a white bath towel 60 cm by 120 cm • a brown bath towel 60 cm by 120 cm
• a small piece of white towelling material or a piece of white cotton (for the ears of the facecloth-puppet)
• brown thread, a little darker than the colour of the towel

Equipment

• a sewing machine • a pair of sewing scissors • pins

Gazelle lamp

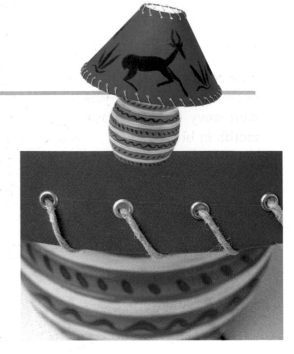

*O*n this blue and orange lamp, three lively, elegant gazelles watch over you as you sleep.

Making the gazelle stencil

• Photocopy the design, increasing its size as required.

• Place the photocopy below the adhesive film and cut it out using a Stanley knife.

Leaf motif

• Using a medium paintbrush, paint leaf motifs freehand between the gazelles.

Applying the stencil

• Remove the backing from the film, and stick it on to the lampshade. Using the stencil brush, apply the undiluted black paint, tapping it on lightly so the paint does not seep behind the stencil. Try this out on a piece of paper first to perfect.

• Carefully remove the film, checking that the paint is dry before painting the second gazelle. Measure the shade so that the three gazelles are equally spaced around the lampshade.

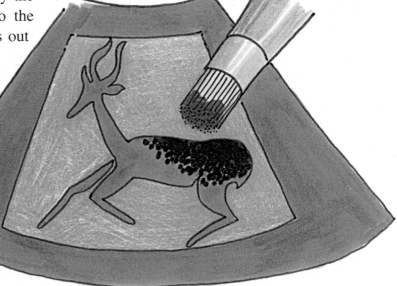

Painting the lampbase

• Decorate the lampbase by alternating stripes of yellow with wavy lines and dash motifs in blue.

String detail

• Affix the metal

eyelets around the top and bottom of the lampshade, 1.5 centimetres from the edge, at intervals of 2.5 centimetres.

• Thread the string through the holes as shown in the diagram.

• Finish off by knotting the two ends of the string together on the inside of the lampshade.

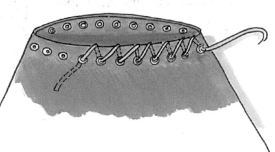

Materials

• a ceramic lampstand, preferably in orange • a blue fabric lampshade • yellow and blue ceramic paints
• black fabric paint
• transparent adhesive film• small metal eyelets
• a ball of string

Equipment

• a stencil brush (flat, round brush) • a medium paintbrush
• a Stanley knife

Zebra tray

*T*he striking stripes of the zebra give this design a fresh appeal, and make an attractive tray.

Creating the design

There are two ways to achieve this effect:

1) Paint the design on to paper, cardboard or fabric. Place this on to the tray and cover it with a piece of glass or plexiglas to keep it clean.

or

2) Paint the design directly on to a wooden or metal tray. In this case, prepare the tray by applying two coats of dark paint, sanding the first coat before applying the second.

Once the design is complete, leave the tray for a few days to dry completely before applying clear varnish to protect it.

• Sketch out the design, or trace the design lightly. Do not make the outlines strong. Then, with a large paintbrush, apply the light paint in zebra stripes. Use large brushstrokes to give the natural stripes.

You may need to practise on some paper to get the hang of this.

Materials

• a wooden tray • drawing paper (220 g) in a dark colour (dark blue, red or black) • gouache or acrylic paint in a light, bright colour

Equipment

• a fairly thick watercolour brush

Leopard frieze

*L*eopards leap through this stencilled frieze.

Making the stencil

• Draw your chosen design on to the cardboard. Cut out the shape using a Stanley knife.

• Position the stencil on the area to be stencilled, and tape it in place.

Painting

• Using the stencil brush, apply the yellow paint to fill the shape of the leopard. Make the top part of the shape a little darker.

• With the fine paintbrush apply the dark spots of the leopard's coat.

• Alternate different silhouettes to complete the frieze.

Materials

• thick circular piece of cardboard (approximately 2 mm thick) to make stencil
• yellow and white gouache paints • dark-coloured gouache paint (black, or dark sepia) • adhesive tape

Equipment

• stencil brush (flat, round brush) • a fine paintbrush
• a Stanley knife

Serpent bell

*M*ake the infamous rattlesnake into a useful gilded bell.

Preparing the spring

• Take the spring and saw it in half, angling the saw to produce a sharp end to the spring.

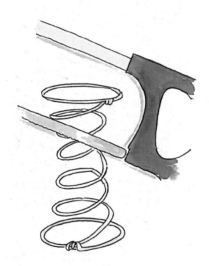

Making the snake

• Take a piece of Fimo modelling clay and knead it to soften it. Roll this piece out on the pastry board with the palm of your hand to create a sausage-shape, 1.5 cm in diameter and 10 cm long, tapered at one end.

• Form a head at the thick end, and cut the mouth of the snake with the Stanley knife.

• Roll a small piece of modelling clay to make the tongue (cut a fork in the tongue along about half of its length) and attach.

• Form two small balls of clay for the eyes.

• Lightly pierce the clay with a pencil to form the two eyes and the nostrils.

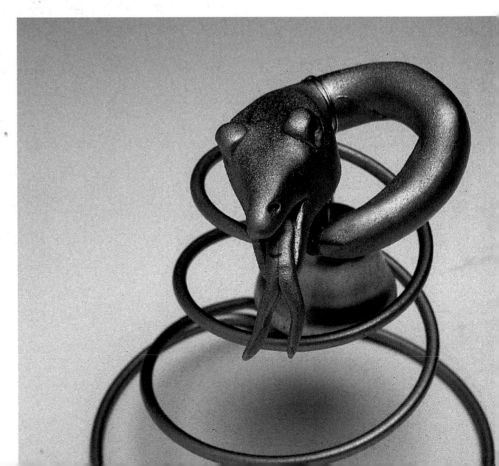

Assembly

• Stick the spring into the tail of the snake, about 2 cm deep. Curl the snake so that the head is positioned in the centre of the spring.

If the head is too heavy, balance it above the spring on a small metal spoon.

Cooking

• Place the whole thing on a sheet of aluminium foil and cook it in an oven, following the instructions for the modelling clay.

Completing the project

• Allow the snake to cool and glue it in place on the spring, then spray the whole thing with gold paint.

• Finally, take the gold thread, loop it through the chain of the bell, and hang it around the snake's neck.

• Your serpent bell is ready for use!

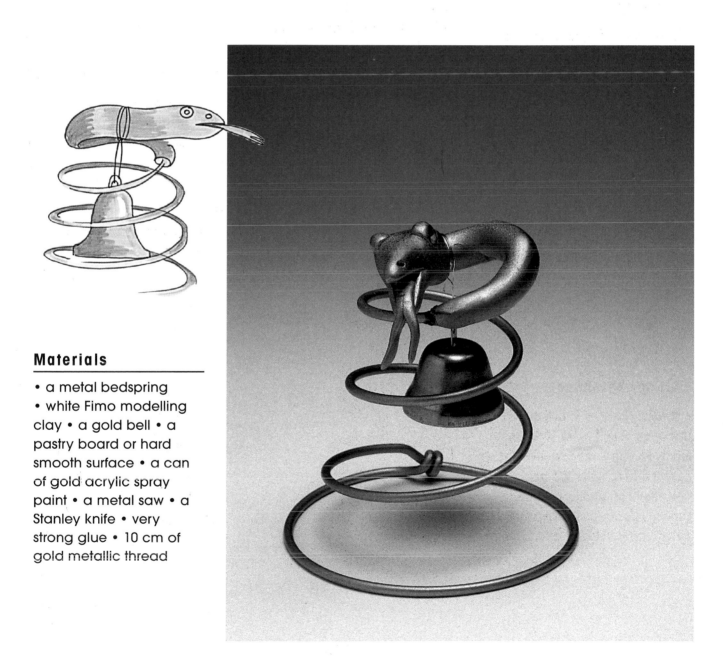

Materials

• a metal bedspring
• white Fimo modelling clay • a gold bell • a pastry board or hard smooth surface • a can of gold acrylic spray paint • a metal saw • a Stanley knife • very strong glue • 10 cm of gold metallic thread

Photographic credits

Colibri: G. Bonnafous: 54c; R. Leguen: 17a; J.L. Paumard: 73b; M. Rohr: 33; C. Simon: 8c, 10-11, 63b; R. Toulouse: 55b

Jacana: 60b, 80a

Nature: 41a, 62b; Berthoule: 69a; Hervé Chaumeton: 24b, 34b, 36a, 37b, 42a, 49a, 50, 65b, 81, 66a, 74a, 75a; Chaumeton/D.S. Berthon: 12a; Chaumeton/Chana: 6a, 46a; Chaumeton/Hellio: 67, 68c; Chaumeton/Lanceau: 47b, 61, 64a, 75b; Chaumeton/Samba: 22b, 47a; Choussy: 62c; Couderc: 51; Dalton/NHPA: 14-15; Ferrero: 56a, 57b, 58-59, 66b, 69b, 68a, 70-71; François Gohier: 18a, 18b, 19b, 20a, 30a, 31a, 31b, 77; Grospas: 24a, 25, 32a, 37a, 56c, 57a, 72b, 73a; Krasnodebski: 9, 12c, 62a; Lanceau: 8a; Lanceau/Visage: 8b; Mayet: 36b; Fritz Polking: 6b, 6c, 22a, 23, 28, 28-29, 30b, 35, 38, 38-39, 40, 41b, 42b, 43; Prevot: 32c; Reille: 63a; Samba: 60a, 68b; F. Sauer: 12b, 32b, 48-49, 49b, 64b, 65a, 74b; R. Siegel: 13a; La Tourette: 80b

Okapia: Joe Cancalosi: 26b (1990); Joe Mc Donald: 21, 26a, 27; Clem Haagner: 34c (1991); Dr. Hermann Brehm: 17b

Phone: Collection " J ": 34a; J.P. Ferrero: 56b; J.P. Ferrero/J.M. Labat: 7b, 46b; François Gohier: 20b; Ian Gordon/Auscape: 52a, 52b; M. Grenet/A. Soumillard: 72a; Hannu Hautala: 76-77, 78; J.F Hellio/N. Van Ingen: 44a, 44b, 45; Claude Jardel: 16; Labat/Jardel: 15; Hans Reinhard: 79; Mark Spencer/Auscape: 53; Raymond Valter: 13b; Albert Visage: 72c

Acknowledgements

The publishers would like to thank all those who have contributed to this book, in particular:
Antoine Caron, Michèle Forest, Nicolas Lemaire, Hervé Levano, Kha Luan Pham,
Vincent Pompougnac, Marie-Laure Sers-Besson, Emmanuelle Zumstein

Illustration: Franz Rey
Translation: Mickael Mayor, Sarah Snake